A Dance of Happy Discovery

Lively Lila

By Ben Levey

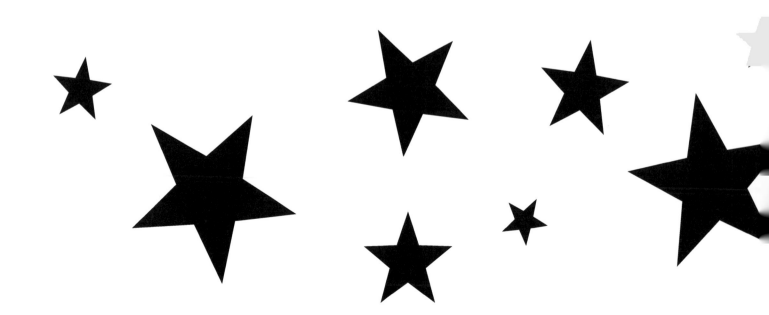

FOR JEN

TINY TREE

First Published in 2024 by
Tiny Tree Books

www.tinytreebooks.com

ISBN: 9781837914647

Meet Lively Lila, a girl full of zest,
whose thoughts take her on an adventurous quest.
With **ADHD** as her friendly guide,
she dances through life, her spirit undenied.

In a world of colours where chaos finds peace,
Lila's imagination never seems to cease.
From **PIRATES** to **FAIRIES**, her mind takes flight
with creativity soaring, shining bright.

Sometimes, it's difficult for people to understand;
Lila's mind moves quickly, like shifting sand.
But with **PATIENCE** and **KINDNESS** hearts can unite,
embracing her quirks, bringing joy and light.

There are moments when Lila needs a little aid;
when taking medication can make the noise fade.
It helps her **FOCUS**, giving her mind a release,
letting her navigate life with greater peace.

In Lila's world, there are times when she needs a break;
a quiet moment to **BREATHE, REALIGN** and **DEFLATE**.
A cosy corner and gentle retreat
where she can recharge and feel complete.

Lila's journey is filled with ups and downs
but she never lets her spirits frown.
For her, **ADHD** is a part of who she is
and she finds strength amidst the occasional **QUIZ**.

She's taught her friends about **EMPATHY** and **CARE**,
about embracing differences and being aware.
They celebrate her quirks and her unique way,
learning from Lila each and every day.

Lila's adventures teach her not to feel bad,

for she's a **SUPERSTAR**, **UNIQUE** and **RAD**.

With her quick-witted mind and vibrant soul,

she constantly shines, reaching every goal.

Her teachers and parents provide **SUPPORT** and **LOVE**,
understanding her needs like a hand in a glove.
Together, they create a nurturing space
where Lila can thrive and find her place.

Lila knows that her worth is never defined
by the moments when her mind gets entwined.
She's taught to embrace her **STRENGTHS** and **SKILLS**
as her true potential unfolds and thrills.

So, to all the children like Lively Lila out there,
embrace your journey for it's a story to share.
Be **PROUD** of who you are, both inside and out,
and let your vibrant spirit sing and shout.

In Lively Lila's world full of wonder and delight,
her ADHD is a **SUPERPOWER** shining ever so bright.
With love and acceptance her journey unfurls,
inspiring others to embrace their own worlds.

In my world, you see,
it's not just about me;
there are many other
people with **ADHD**.

If you care for them,
then here is the key:
Patience and love,
UNCONDITIONALLY.